Grandma's Story

MOIRA BUTTERFIELD   illustrated by SALVATORE RUBBINO

WALKER BOOKS
AND SUBSIDIARIES

LONDON • BOSTON • SYDNEY • AUCKLAND

When you were born
you opened your eyes,
you wiggled your toes
and you started making your life story.
It's all the things that happen to you
and all the things you say and do.

All the grown-ups you know have *their* own story.

They were all babies once.

Then they grew,

just like you.

My life story
has you in it.

You could ask one of the grown-ups that you know a question about their life story, like: *Where did you live when you were little?*

I grew up on a farm. I used to help feed the chickens.

I grew up in a house around the corner.
I can see the roof from here.

I grew up across the sea.
It's a plane ride away.

What food did you like when you were small?

Which food didn't you like at all?

My grandma made the best pasta sauce.
I'll show you how to make it too.

At school we ate cold grey lumps. They called it stew.

I liked sweet oranges from the tree outside my bedroom.

Did you have a toy that you liked best?

I had a little guitar with
painted flowers on it. Here it is!

I had a teddy that was bigger than me.

I had a doll with a golden dress.

Did you have a pet that you helped to look after?

I had a cat called Leo.
He looked like a little ginger lion.

I had a tortoise called Hercules.
He once ate the neighbour's lettuce.

I had a rabbit called Misha.
She once nibbled my school socks!

Ask the grown-ups that you know if they have photos from years ago that show them back when they were younger, a while ago in their stories.

Your grandparents were once babies and did the things that babies do, like crying, sleeping and wanting hugs.

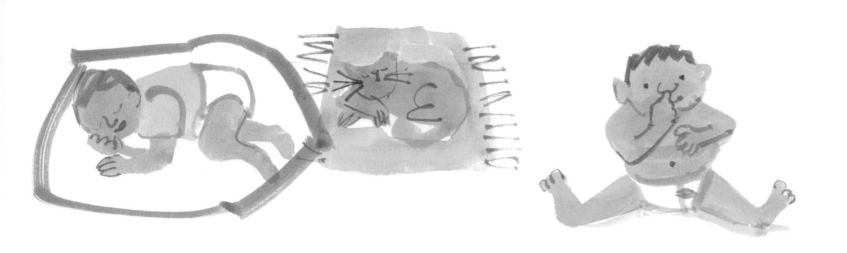

Everyone you know was a baby, and their grandparents were babies.

Babies, babies, babies ... right back

through time to the beginning of people.

As all the babies grew and grew, they learnt new things to do.

And so will you.

And your story will grow and grow and be wonderful.

I'm glad that I'm in your story,
and I'm very glad that you're in mine!

Some ideas for sharing personal stories

When children begin to learn about history start them off by getting them to talk to adults they know about life in the past. It will give them a sense of time as well as connecting them positively to other generations around them.

→ You could help your child choose from extended family members, neighbours or friendly people your child knows in their community.

→ Encourage children to ask questions about aspects of life they know themselves – such as food or toys.

→ Asking three or four questions tends to work best, so children don't get overloaded with information and there will be plenty of time for chatting about each answer.

Here are some suggested questions. Your child might have their own question ideas, too.

When you were the same age as me ...

What toys did you like playing with?

Did you have a hobby?

What food did you like best? What didn't you like?

What did your home look like?

What was your favourite lesson at school?

Did you have a pet?

What were your favourite clothes?

I had a toy aeroplane.

I liked
building
dens.

My favourite dress
was the colour of lemons.

I had a tabby cat
called Minky.

First published 2022 by Walker Books Ltd
87 Vauxhall Walk, London SE11 5HJ

This edition published 2023

2 4 6 8 10 9 7 5 3 1

Text © 2022 Moira Butterfield
Illustrations © 2022 Salvatore Rubbino

This book has been typeset in Woodland ITC

Printed in China

British Library Cataloguing in Publication Data:
a catalogue record for this book is available from the British Library

ISBN 978-1-5295-1335-6

www.walker.co.uk